ONE MORE TIME 8

Irish & Scottish Favourites

C000175512

Arranged by Steve Clark
Edited by Peter Foss
First Published 1990
International Music Publications

Exclusive Distributors
International Music Publications
Southend Road, Woodford Green,
Essex IG8 8HN, England

*Front Cover photographs: View towards Clew Bay, County
Mayo, Eire. Loch Lomond, Dumbartonshire, Scotland.*

215-2-607

Medley 1

IT'S A GREAT DAY FOR THE IRISH

Words and Music
by RODGER EDENS

It's a great day   for the I - rish,

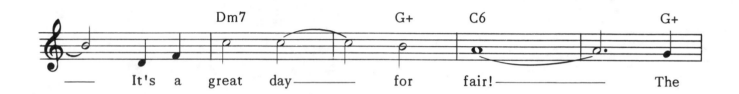

It's a great day   for fair!   The

side - walks of New York are thick with Blar - ney,   For

sure you'd think New York was old Kil - lar - ney!   It's a

great day   for the Sham - rock,   For the

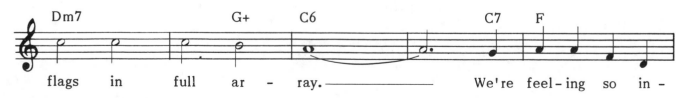

flags in full ar - ray.   We're feel - ing so in -

-spir-ish, sure be-cause for all the I-rish, It's a great,

great — day. It's a day. "Hel-

PATSY FAGAN

Words and Music
by THOMAS P. KEENAN

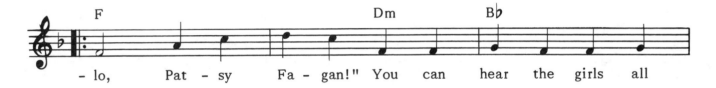

-lo, Pat-sy Fa-gan!" You can hear the girls all

cry. "Hel-lo, Pat-sy Fa-gan, you're the ap-ple of me

eye. You're a de-cent boy from Ire-land, there's no-one can de-

-ny, You're a rar-em tar-em div-il-may car-em

de-cent I-rish boy." "Hel-boy." There was

DELANEY'S DONKEY

Words and Music
by WILLIAM HARGREAVES

Ri - ley push-ing it, shov-ing it and shushing it, Ho-gan, Lo-gan, ev-'ry-one in town, Lined up at-tack-ing it shov-ing it and smack-ing it; They might as well have tried to push the Town Hall down. The don-key was eye-ing them, o-pen-ly de-fy-ing them, Wink-ing, blink-ing, twist-ing out of place, Ri-ley re-vers-ing it, ev-'ry-bo-dy cursing it, The day De-laney's donkey ran the half mile race. With my shil -

WITH MY SHILLELAGH UNDER MY ARM

Words and Music by
BILLY O'BRIEN & RAYMOND WALLACE

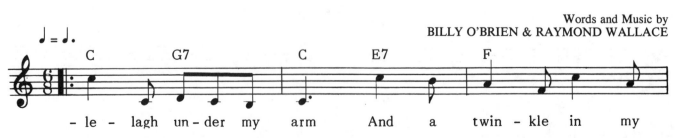

- le - lagh un-der my arm And a twin-kle in my

Medley 2

THE ROSE OF TRALEE

Words by C. M. SPENCER
Music by C. W. GLOVER

1. The pale moon was ris - ing a - bove the green
cool shades of eve - ning their man - tle were

moun - tain, The sun was de - clin - ing be - neath the blue
spread-ing, And Ma - ry all smil - ing was list - 'ning to

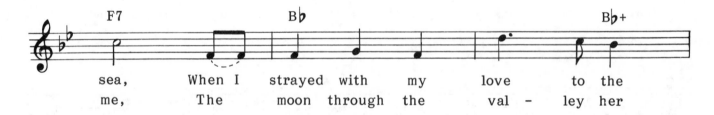

sea, When I strayed with my love to the
me, The moon through the val - ley her

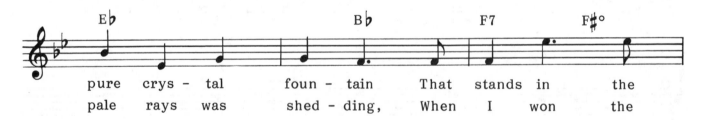

pure crys - tal foun - tain That stands in the
pale rays was shed - ding, When I won the

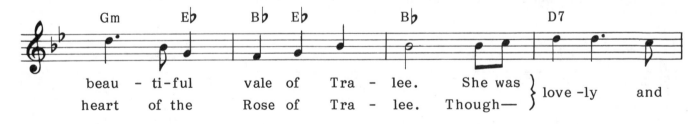

beau - ti - ful vale of Tra - lee. She was
heart of the Rose of Tra - lee. Though— } love -ly and

fair as the rose of— the— sum - mer, Yet 'twas not her

beau - ty a - lone that won me, Oh, no! 'twas the

truth in her eye ev - er dawn-ing, That made me love

Ma - ry, the Rose of Tra - lee. 2.The -lee.

KATHLEEN MAVOURNEEN

TRADITIONAL

Kath - leen Ma - vour - neen The grey dawn is

break-ing,—— The horn of the hun-ter is—

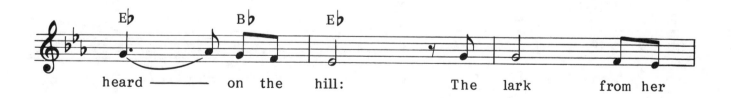

heard —— on the hill: The lark from her

light wing the bright —— dew is shak —— ing,—

WHEN IRISH EYES ARE SMILING

Words by CHAUNCEY OLCOTT and GEO GRAFF Jr
Music by ERNEST R BALL

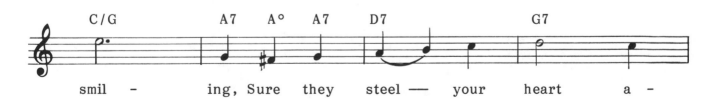

COCKLES AND MUSSELS

TRADITIONAL

Dub - lin's fair ci - ty, where the girls are so
died of a fev - er and no one could

pret - ty, I first set my eyes on sweet
save her, And first that was my the end of sweet

Mol - ly Ma - lone; As she wheeled her wheel -
Mol - ly Ma - lone; Her ghost wheels her

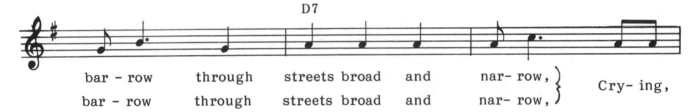

bar - row through streets broad and nar- row, } Cry - ing,
bar - row through streets broad and nar- row, }

"Cock - les and mus - sels a - live, a - live

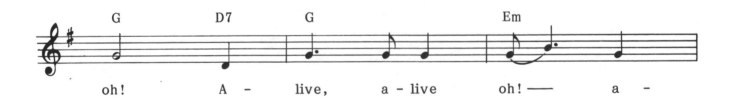

oh! A - live, a - live oh! — a -

live, a - live oh!" — Cry-ing, "Cock - les and

mus - sels a - live, a - live oh!" 2.She oh!"

Medley 3

THE IRISH ROVER

TRADITIONAL

In the

year of our Lord eigh - teen hun - dred and six We set

sail from the coal quay of Cork, We were sail - ing a - way with a

car - go of bricks For the grand ci - ty hall in New York. We'd an

el - e-gant craft, it was rigged fore and aft And how the trade winds

drove —— her; She had twen - ty three masts and she stood sev-'ral blasts And they

called her the Ir - ish rov - er. In the rov - er. Have you

PHIL THE FLUTER

Words and Music by
PERCY FRENCH & DAVID HENEKER

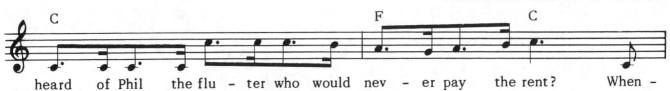

heard of Phil the flu - ter who would nev - er pay the rent? When -

- ev - er he was down and out with - out a sin - gle cent, He would

cir - cu - late a no - tice to his neigh - bours one and all As to

how he'd like their com - pan - y that eve - ning at the ball. And

when writ - ing out he was care - ful to sug - gest to them, That

if they found a hat of his con - ven - ient to the door; The

more they put in, when - ev - er he re - quest - ed them The

bet - ter would the mu - sic be for bat - ter - ing the floor. With the

toot of the flute and the twid - dle of the fid - dle, Oh!

Hop - ping in the mid - dle like a her - ring on the grid - dle, Oh!

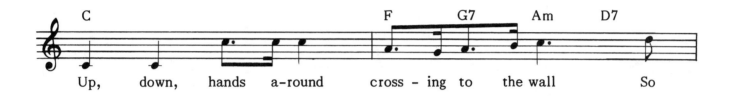

Up, down, hands a-round cross - ing to the wall So

come and join the gai - et - y at Phil the

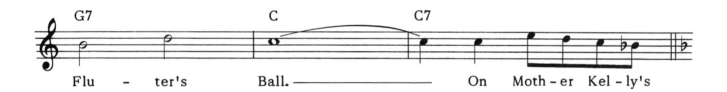

Flu - ter's Ball. On Moth - er Kel -ly's

ON MOTHER KELLY'S DOORSTEP

Words and Music
by GEO. A. STEVEN

door - step, down Par - a - dise Row,

I'd sit - a - long o' Nel - ly, She'd sit a - long o'

© 1925 & 1990 Francis Day & Hunter Ltd, London WC2H 0EA

used to, On Moth-er Kel-ly's door - step, —

down Par-a-dise Row. —

FLANAGAN

Words and Music by
C. W. MURPHY and WILL LETTERS

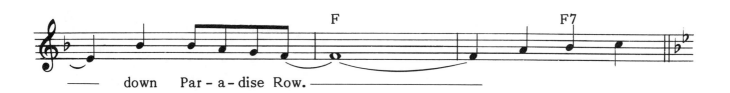

Flan - a-gan, Flan - a-gan, Take me to the Isle of

Man a-gain. Take me where the folks all cry,

K - E - dou-ble-L - Y! Flan - a-gan, Flan - a-gan, If you

love your Ma - ry Ann, Oh! — Flan-a-gan,

Take me to the Isle of Man. Man.

Medley 4

THE LAST ROSE OF SUMMER

TRADITIONAL

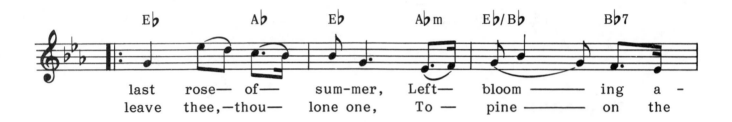

last rose— of— sum-mer, Left— bloom———ing a -
leave thee,—thou— lone one, To — pine ——— on the

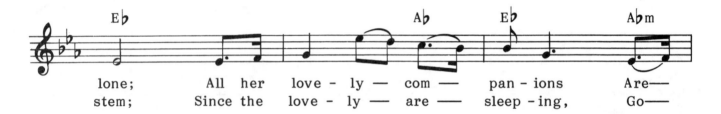

lone; All her love - ly — com — pan - ions Are—
stem; Since the love - ly — are — sleep -ing, Go—

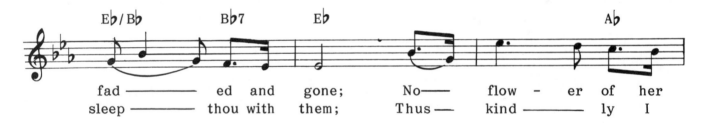

fad————ed and gone; No—— flow - er of her
sleep ——— thou with them; Thus— kind ——— ly I

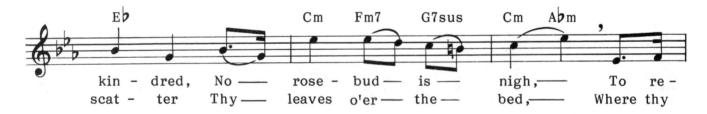

kin — dred, No —— rose - bud — is — nigh,—— To re-
scat - ter Thy— leaves o'er — the — bed,—— Where thy

flect back— her— blush-es Or — give ——— sigh for
mates of — the — gar-den Lie — scent ——— less and

sigh. 2.I'll not dead. 1.There

THE WILD COLONIAL BOY

Words and Music
by JOSEPH M CROFTS

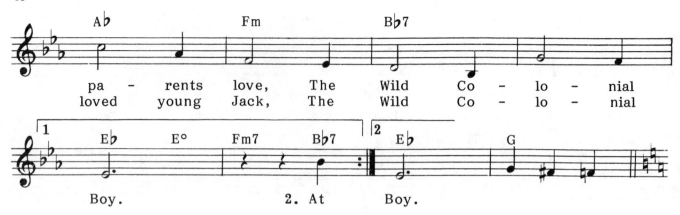

pa - rents love, The Wild Co - lo - nial
loved young Jack, The Wild Co - lo - nial

Boy.   2. At   Boy.

HOW CAN YOU BUY KILLARNEY?

Words and Music by HAMILTON KENNEDY,
FREDDIE GRUNDLAND, GERALD MORRISON & TED STEELS

How can you buy all the stars in the skies?

How can you buy two blue I - rish eyes?

How can you pur - chase a fond mo - ther's sighs?

How can you buy Kil - lar - ney?

Na - ture be - stowed all her gifts with a smile, The

em - 'rald, the sham - rock, the blar - ney.

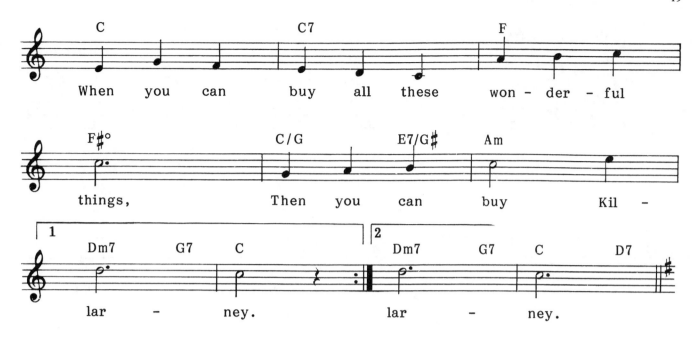

C **C7** **F**
When you can buy all these won - der - ful

F#° **C/G** **E7/G#** **Am**
things, Then you can buy Kil -

1 **Dm7** **G7** **C** **2** **Dm7** **G7** **C** **D7**
lar - ney. lar - ney.

THE SPINNING WHEEL

Words & Music by
JOHN FRANCIS WALLER & DELIA MURPHY

G
Mer - ri - ly, cheer - i - ly, nois - i - ly

D7
whir - ring Swings the wheel, spins the wheel while the foot's

G **G7**
stir - ring; Spright - ly and light - ly and

C **G** **D7**
air - i - ly ring - ing, Sounds the sweet

G **D7** **G**
voice of the young maid - en sing - ing.

Medley 5

DANNY BOY

TRADITIONAL

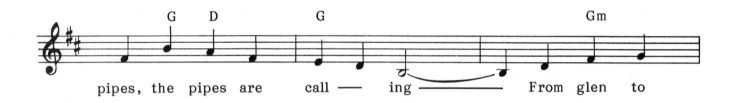

O Dan - ny boy, the

pipes, the pipes are call — ing ——— From glen to

glen, and down the moun - tain side; ———————

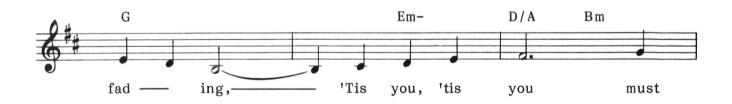

——— The sum - mer's gone, and all the ros - es

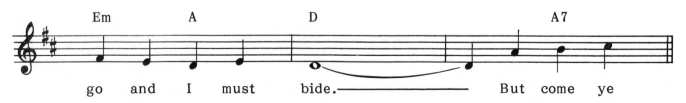

fad — ing, ——————— 'Tis you, 'tis you must

go and I must bide. ——————— But come ye

DID YOUR MOTHER COME FROM IRELAND

Words and Music by
JIMMY KENNEDY & MICHAEL CARR

THE ISLE OF INNISFREE

Words and Music by RICHARD FARRELLY

A LITTLE BIT OF HEAVEN

Words by J KEIRN BRENNAN
Music by ERNEST R BALL

lit - tle bit of Hea - ven fell from out the sky one day,——— And—

nest - led on the o - cean in a spot so far a- way;——— And

when the An - gels found it, Sure it looked so sweet and fair,——— They

said sup-pose we leave it, for it looks so peace - ful there: So, they

sprink-led it with star dust just to make the sham-rocks grow;——'Tis the

on - ly place you'll find them no mat-ter where you go;——— Then they

dot - ted it with sil - ver, To make its lakes so grand, And ——

when they had it fin-ished sure they called it Ire — land.

Sub-published by B. Feldman & Co. Ltd., London WC2H 0EA / Redwood Music Ltd., London W1X 2LR

Medley 6

COME BACK TO ERIN

TRADITIONAL

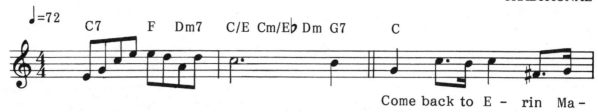

Come back to E - rin Ma -

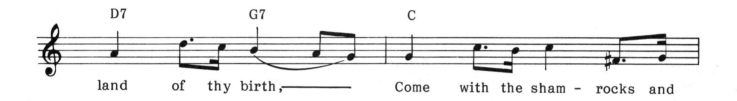

vour - neen, Ma-vour - neen, Come back A - roon, to the

land of thy birth,————— Come with the sham - rocks and

spring-time, Ma-vour-neen, And its Kil-lar-ney shall ring with our mirth.

A little quicker

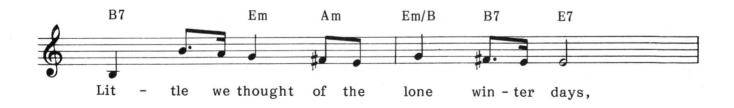

Sure, when we lent ye to beau - ti - ful Eng - land,

Lit - tle we thought of the lone win - ter days,

Lit - tle we thought of the hush of the star - shine

O - ver the moun - tain, the Bluffs and the Brays! Then

Tempo I

come back to E - rin, Ma - vour - neen, Ma - vour - neen,

Come back a - gain to the land of thy birth,———

Come back to E - rin, Ma - vour - neen, Ma-vour - neen,

And— it's Kil - lar — ney shall ring with our mirth. I'll

I'LL TAKE YOU HOME AGAIN KATHLEEN

TRADITIONAL

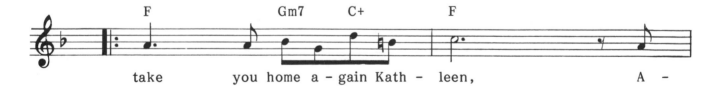

take you home a - gain Kath - leen, A -

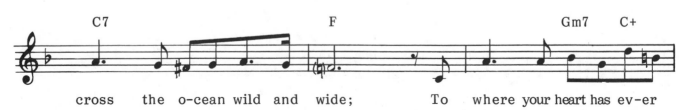

cross the o-cean wild and wide; To where your heart has ev - er

THE MINSTREL BOY

TRADITIONAL

Min - strel boy—— to the war is gone, In the
Min - strel fell,—— but the foe - man's chain Could not

ranks of death—— you'll—— find him, His
bring his proud—— soul —— un - der, The

fa - ther's sword—— he has gird - ed on, And his
harp he love-d nev - er spoke a - gain. For he

wild harp slung —————— be - hind him.
tore its chords———— a - sun - der, And

'Land of Song!' said the war - rior bard, 'Though
said, 'No chains shall —— sul - ley thee, Thou

all the world be - trays —————— thee, One
soul of love and brav - er - y, Thy

sword at least,—— thy —— rights shall guard, One ——
songs were made—— for the pure and free, They shall

faith - ful harp—— shall praise thee.'2.The slave - ry.'
nev - er sound—— in

THE KERRY DANCE

TRADITIONAL

O the days of the Ker - ry danc - ing, O the ring of the

pi - per's tune; O for one of those hours of glad - ness,

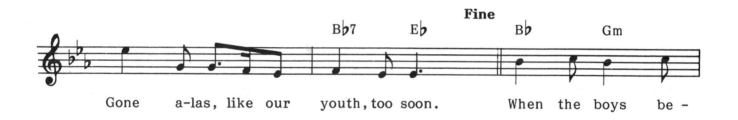

Gone a-las, like our youth, too soon. When the boys be -

gan to gath - er in the glen, of a sum - mer night,

And the ker- ry pi - per's tun -ing made us long—with wild de-light.

O to think of it, O to dream of it, Fills my heart with tears:

Medley 7

IF YOU'RE IRISH COME INTO THE PARLOUR

Words and Music by
SHAUN GLENVILLE & FRANK MILLER

MACNAMARA'S BAND

Words by JOHN J. STAMFORD
Music by SHAMUS O'CONNOR

name is Mac - na - ma - ra, I'm the lead - er of the

band, And though we're small in num - ber we're the

best in all the land. Oh, I am the con -

- duc - tor and we oft - en have to play With

all the best mu - si - cian - ers you hear a - bout to -

- day. When the drums go bang, the cym - bals clang, the

horns will blaze a - way Mac - Car - thy puffs the

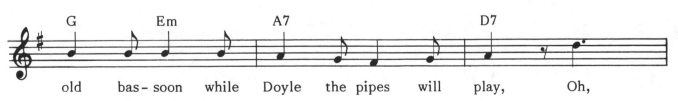

old bas - soon while Doyle the pipes will play, Oh,

Hen-nes-sy Ten-nes-sy too-tles the flute, my word 'tis some-thing grand, Oh, a cred-it to old Ire-land, boys, is Mac-na-ma-ra's band. Tra-la-la la la,—— Tra-la-la la la,—— Tra-la- -la la la la la la la la la,—— Tra-la-la la la,—— Tra-la-la la la,—— Tra-la-la la la la la la la la la la, Tra-la-la la! Let him

LET HIM GO, LET HIM TARRY

go, let him tar-ry, let him sink or let him swim.

He doesn't care for me nor I don't care for him. He can go and get an-oth-er that I

hope he will en-joy, For I'm going to mar-ry a

far nic-er boy. Let him far nic-er boy.

RAKES OF MALLOW

Beau-ing, belle-ing, danc-ing, drink—ing,— Breaking win-dows, curs-ing, sink—ing,—

Ev - er rak - ing, nev - er think-ing, Live—the—Rakes-of— Mal - low.

Spend-ing—fast - er than it comes, Beat-ing—wait -ers, bail-iffs, duns,

Bac-chus'—true be - got - ten sons, Live—the—Rakes-of— Mal - low.

Medley 8

THE WEARIN 'O' THE GREEN

TRADITIONAL

1. O———

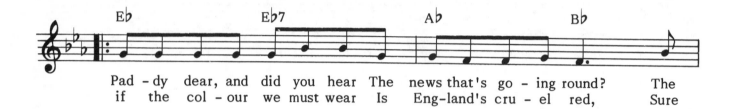

Pad - dy dear, and did you hear The news that's go - ing round? The
if the col - our we must wear Is Eng-land's cru - el red, Sure

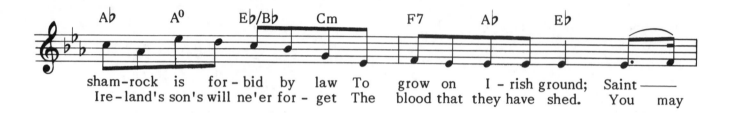

sham-rock is for - bid by law To grow on I - rish ground; Saint———
Ire - land's son's will ne'er for - get The blood that they have shed. You may

Pat - rick's day no more we'll keep, His col - ours can't be seen, For
take the sham-rock from your hat, And cast it on the sod, But

there's a nas - ty law a - gainst The wear - in' o' the green. I———
it'll take root and flour - ish still Though un - der-foot is trod. When———

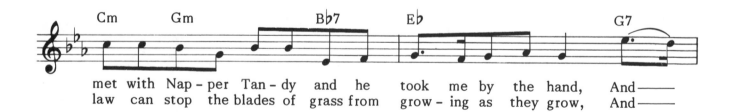

met with Nap - per Tan - dy and he took me by the hand, And———
law can stop the blades of grass from grow - ing as they grow, And———

said, "How's poor old Ire——— land And how——— does she stand?" She's the
when the leaves in sum-mer time Their ver - dure cease to show, Then———

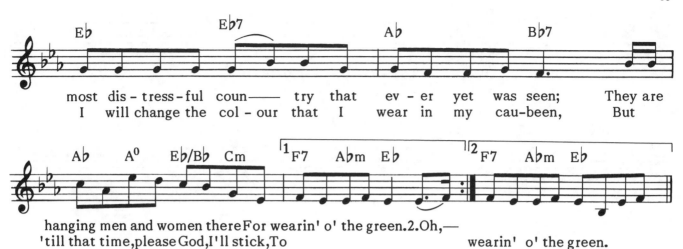

most dis-tress-ful coun——try that ev-er yet was seen; They are
I will change the col-our that I wear in my cau-been, But

hanging men and women thereFor wearin' o' the green.2.Oh,—
'till that time,please God,I'll stick,To   wearin' o' the green.

THAT'S AN IRISH LULLABY

Words and Music
by J. R. SHANNON

O - ver in Kil-ar-ney,—— Ma - ny years a-go,—— My

moth - er sang a song to me In tones so sweet and low, Just a

sim - ple lit - tle dit-ty, In her good old I - rish way, And I'd

give the world if she could sing That song to me this day:——

"Too -ra-loo-ra-loo-ral,—— Too -ra-loo-ra-li, Too -ra-loo -ra-loo-ral,—

Hush, now, don't you cry—— Too - ra-loo-ra-loo-ral, Too-ra-loo - ra-li,

Too - ra-loo - ra-loo-ral, That's an I - rish lul - la-by." 1. O——

THE FOGGY DEW

TRADITIONAL

Ei - leen, my girl, I'd go walk - ing with you Where the
Ei - leen, my girl, you'll re - mem - ber the morn In the

mead——ows are shin-ing with the fog - gy dew; For the
fresh——dew - y mead-ows where our love was born; Sure, I

sound of your voice sweet - ly falls on the air Where the
thought 'twas an an - gel that walked with me there In the

mead——ows are shin-ing with the fog - gy dew. It is sweet there to meet With the
fresh——dew - y meadows where our love was born. O the dear, bless-ed day When we

grass beneath our feet, And to know that we love each oth-er true; }
ling-ered on our way, Mak-ing vows that we loved each other true; }   O——

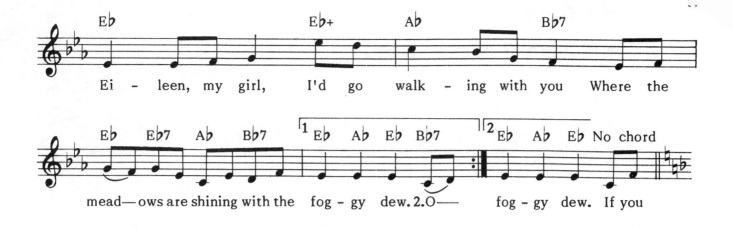

Ei - leen, my girl, I'd go walk - ing with you Where the mead—ows are shining with the fog - gy dew.2.O—— fog - gy dew. If you

GALWAY BAY

Words and Music by
DR. ARTHUR COLAHAN

ev - er go a-cross the sea to Ire - land, Then may-be at the clos-ing of your day, You will sit and watch the moon rise o-ver Clad - dagh, And see the sun go down on Gal-way Bay. Just to hear a-gain the rip-ple of the trout stream, The wo-men in the meadows making hay, And to sit be-side a turf fire in the cab - in, And watch the bare-foot gos-soons at their play. If you play.

Medley 9

THE DEAR LITTLE SHAMROCK

TRADITIONAL

There's a dear lit-tle plant that grows in our Isle, 'Twas Saint Pat-rick him-self sure that set it; And the sun on his la-bour with plea-sure did smile, And the dew from his eye oft-en wet it. It shines through the bog, through the brake, through the mire-land, And he called it the dear lit-tle sham-rock of Ire-land. The

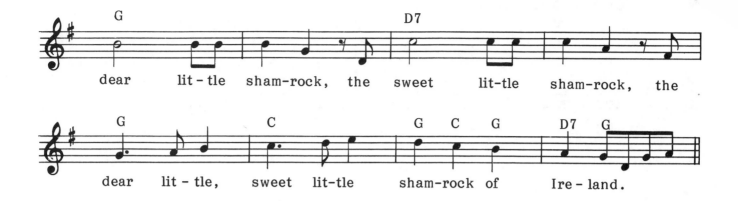

dear lit-tle sham-rock, the sweet lit-tle sham-rock, the

dear lit-tle, sweet lit-tle sham-rock of Ire-land.

SWEET ROSIE O'GRADY

Words and Music
by MAUDE NUGENT

Sweet Ros-ie O'-Gra-dy, My

beau-ti-ful Rose,——— She's my lit-tle

la-dy, That ev-'ry-one knows;———

And when we are mar-ried,

How hap-py we'll be!——— I love sweet

Ros-ie O'-Gra-dy, And Ros-ie O'-

1
G G#° D7

2
G G7

Gra-dy loves me.——— me.——— My

MY WILD IRISH ROSE

1990 International Music Publications, Woodford Green, Essex, IG8 8HN

PEGGY O'NEIL

Words and Music by HARRY PEASE,
ED. G. NELSON & GILBERT DODGE

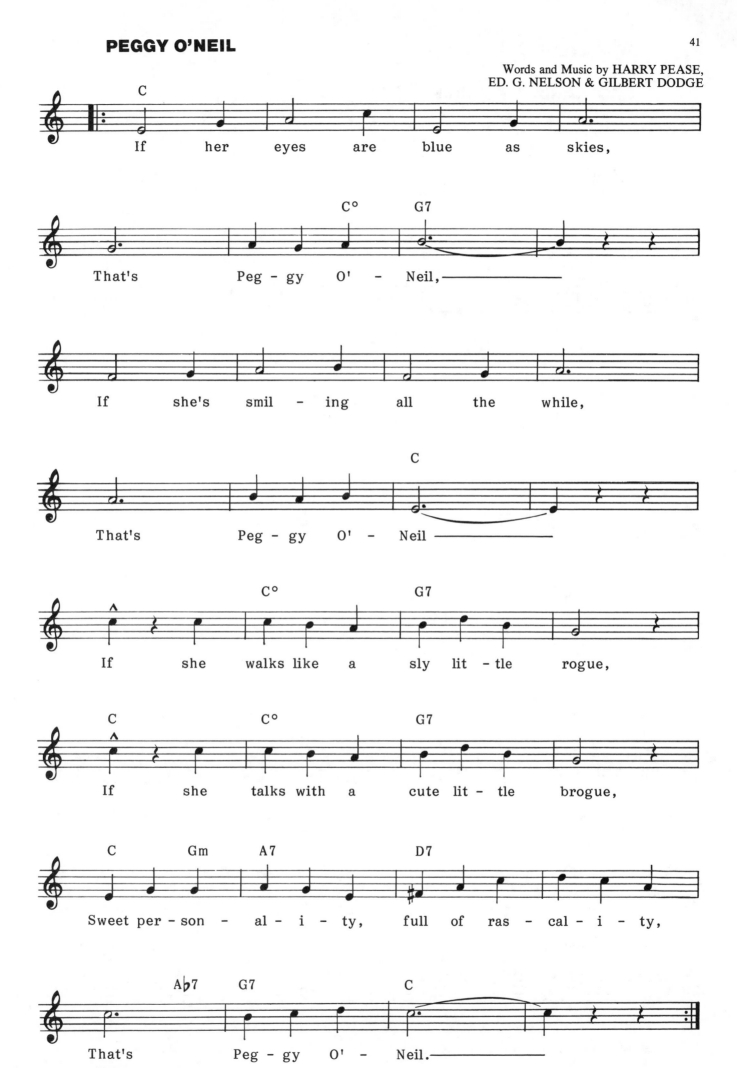

Medley 10

SCOTLAND THE BRAVE

♩ = 96

TRADITIONAL

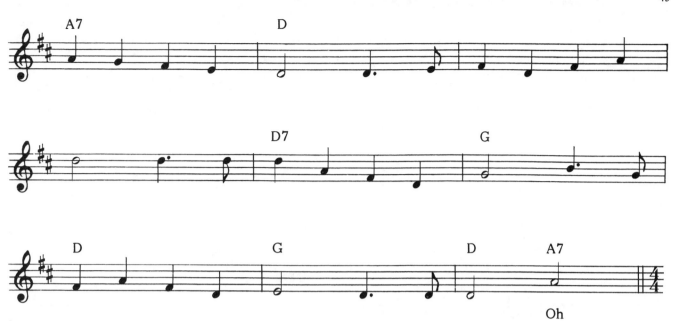

Oh

THE BLUEBELLS OF SCOTLAND

TRADITIONAL

where, tell me where has your—— High - land lad - die gone. Oh where, tell me where has your—— High - land lad - die gone. He's gone with stream-ing ban - ners, where—— no - ble deeds are done, And my sad heart will trem - ble 'til —— he comes safe - ly home. Oh home.

© 1990 International Music Publications, Woodford Green, Essex, IG8 8HN

BONNIE LADDIE, HIGHLAND LADDIE

TRADITIONAL

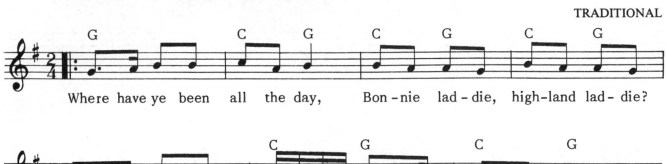

Where have ye been all the day, Bon - nie lad - die, high - land lad - die?

Saw ye him that's far— a—way,—— Bon - nie lad - die,

high - land lad - die? On his head a bon—net—blue, Bon - nie lad - die,

high - land lad - die, Tar - tan plaid and high—land—trew,—— Bon - nie lad - die,

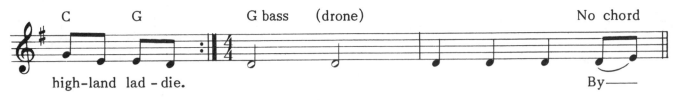

high - land lad - die.   By——

LOCH LOMOND

TRADITIONAL

yon bon-nie banks and by yon bon-nie braes, Where the sun shines bright on Loch
you'll take the high road And I'll take the low road, And I'll be in Scot-land be -

Lo - mond, Where me and my true love were ev - er wont to gae, On the
- fore you; But me and my true love will nev-er meet a-gain On the

bon-nie, bon-nie banks of Loch Lo - mond. O——
bon-nie, bon-nie banks of Loch   Lo - mond.

Medley 11

BONNIE DUNDEE

TRADITIONAL

DOWN IN THE GLEN

Words and Music by
HARRY GORDON and TOMMIE CONNOR

'home.' The sheep are in the fold And there's

peace worth more than gold, For a shep - herd in that

hea- ven Down in the glen. At glen. On the

ON THE BANKS OF ALLAN WATER

TRADITIONAL

banks of Al - lan Wa - ter, when the sweet spring-time did—

fall, — Was the mil - ler's love-ly daugh-ter, fair-est of them

all. For his bride a sol-dier sought her, and a

win - ning tongue had he;— On the banks of Al-lan Wa - ter,

none so gay as she. On the she.

I BELONG TO GLASGOW

Words and Music
by WILL FYFFE

Medley 12

THE END OF THE ROAD

Words and Music by
WILLIAM DILLON and HARRY LAUDER

THE HUNDRED PIPERS

COCK O' THE NORTH

TRADITIONAL

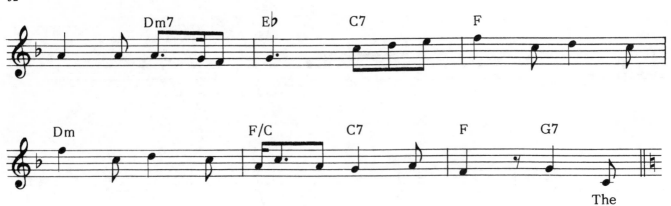

THE CAMPBELLS ARE COMIN'

TRADITIONAL

Medley 13

I KNOW WHERE I'M GOIN'

Words and Music
by HERBERT HUGHES

♩ = 100

I know where I'm go - ing and I know who's go - ing with me, I know who I love, But the Lord knows who I'll mar - ry. I have stock-ings of silk and shoes of bright green leath - er, Combs to put in my hair and a ring for ev - 'ry fin - ger. fin - ger.

WILL YE NO COME BACK AGAIN?

TRADITIONAL

Bon - nie Char - lie noo a - way; Safe - ly owre the friend - ly main; Mo - ny a heart will break in twa, Should he ne'er come back again?

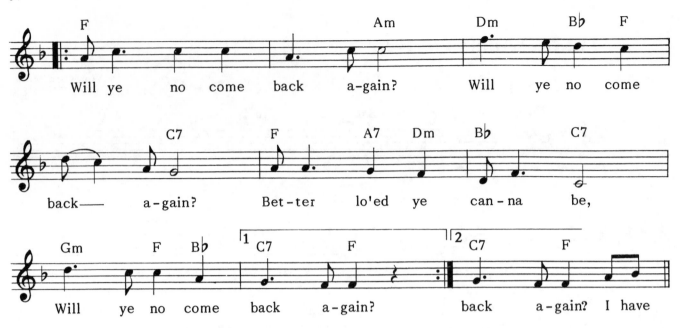

Will ye no come back a-gain? Will ye no come back a-gain? Bet-ter lo'ed ye can-na be, Will ye no come back a-gain? back a-gain? I have

BONNY MARY OF ARGYLE

TRADITIONAL

heard the ma-vis sing-ing His love song to the morn; I have seen the dew-drop cling-ing To the rose just new-ly born. But a sweet-er song has cheered me At the eve-ning's gen-tle close And I've seen an eye still bright-er Than the dew-drop on the rose. 'Twas thy

voice   my   gen - tle   Ma - ry, ———   And   thine   art - less   win - ning

smile   That ———   made   this   world   an   E - den,   Bon - ny

Ma - ry   of— Ar - gyle.   I   have - gyle.   O   my

MY LOVE IS LIKE A RED, RED ROSE

TRADITIONAL

love   is   like   a   red,   red   rose   That's   new - ly   sprung   in   June,   O   my—

love   is   like   a   mel - o - dy   That's   sweet - ly   played   in   tune.   As

fair   art   thou,   my   bon - nie   lass,   so   deep   in   love   am   I; ———   And ———

I   will   love   thee   still,   my   dear,   'Till   all   the   seas   gang   dry;   'Till

all   the   seas   gang   dry,   my   love,   'Till   all   the   seas   gang   dry.   And ———

I   will   love   thee   still, my   dear, 'Till   all   the   seas   gang   dry. O   my   all   the   seas   gang   dry.

© 1990 International Music Publications, Woodford Green, Essex, IG8 8HN

Medley 14

CHARLIE IS MY DARLING

TRADITIONAL

♩=108   Cm   G7   Cm   G7   Cm

Oh!

Cm   Fm   Cm

Char-lie is my dar - ling, my dar - ling, my dar - ling, Oh!

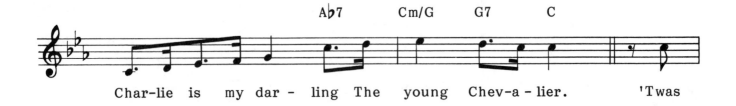

A♭7   Cm/G   G7   C

Char-lie is my dar - ling The young Chev-a - lier.   'Twas

G7   Cm   G7   Cm   B♭

on a Mon-day morn— ing, Right ear-ly in the year   When

E♭   A♭   E♭   Fm   Cm   G7

Char-lie came to our— town, The— young— Chev-a - lier.   Oh!—

C   Fm   C

Char-lie is my dar - ling, my dar - ling, my dar - ling, Oh!

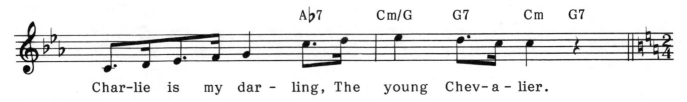

A♭7   Cm/G   G7   Cm   G7

Char-lie is my dar - ling, The young Chev-a - lier.

I LOVE A LASSIE

Words by HARRY LAUDER and GERALD GRAFTON
Music by HARRY LAUDER

I love a las - sie, a bon - nie, bon - nie las - sie, She's as pure as the li - ly in the dell. — — She's as sweet as the heath - er, The bon - nie bloom - ing heath - er; Ma - ry, my Scotch Blue - bell. bell. Then it's

THE TARTAN

Words by SYDNEY BELL
Music by KENNETH McKELLAR

hey! for the tar - tan and ho! for the tar - tan, The stamp 'o' the High - lands from Skye to Dun - dee; And it's proud I am bear - ing the

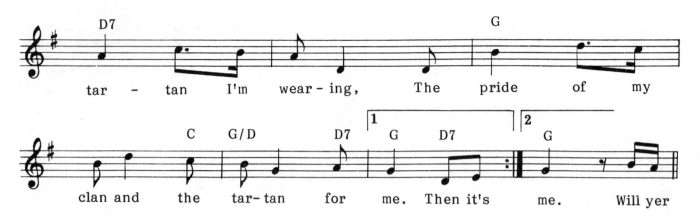

STOP YER TICKLING, JOCK!

Words by HARRY LAUDER and FRANK FOLLOY
Music by HARRY LAUDER

Medley 15

ROBIN ADAIR

TRADITIONAL

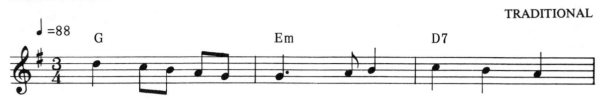

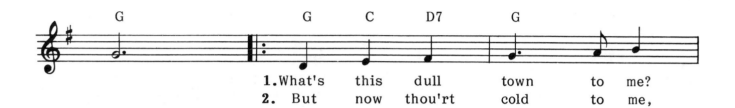

1.What's this dull town to me?
2. But now thou'rt cold to me,

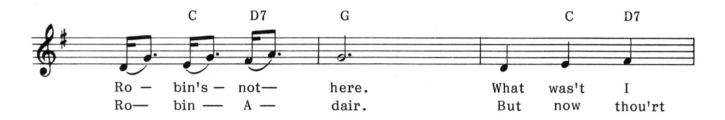

Ro — bin's — not— here.   What was't I
Ro— bin — A — dair.   But now thou'rt

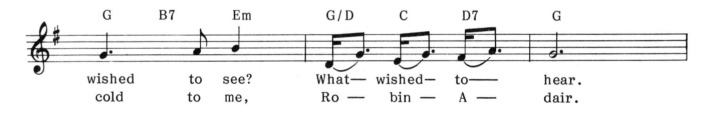

wished to see?   What— wished— to—— hear.
cold to me,   Ro — bin — A — dair.

Where's all the joy and mirth Made this— town a
Yet him I loved so well Still in — my —

Heaven on earth? Oh, they are all — fled with thee,
heart shall dwell; Oh, I — can — ne'er for - get

Ro— bin— A — dair.   dair. Ye
Ro— bin— A —

YE BANKS AND BRAES O'BONNIE DOON

TRADITIONAL

THE SKYE BOAT SONG

TRADITIONAL

Speed bon-nie boat, like a bird on the wing,

On - ward the sail - ors cry.————

Car - ry the lad that is born to be king,

O - ver the sea to Skye.————

Loud the winds howl, Loud the waves roar,

thun - der-claps rend the air,————

Baf - fled our foes stand on the shore,

Fol - low they will not dare.————

Speed bon-nie boat, like a bird on the wing,

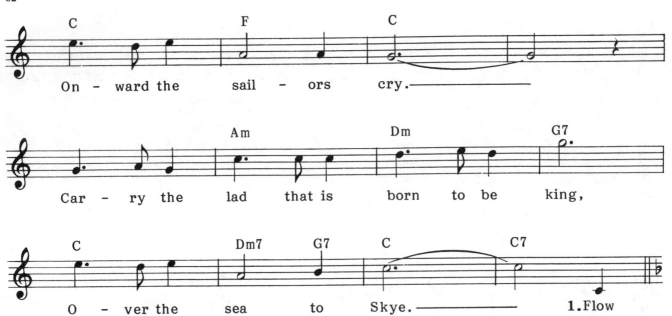

C On-ward the sail-ors cry. **F** **C**

Am Car-ry the lad that is born to be king, **Dm** **G7**

C O-ver the sea to Skye. **Dm7** **G7** **C** **C7** 1.Flow

AFTON WATER

TRADITIONAL

F gen-tly, sweet— Af-ton, a— mong thy green— **Gm7** **Dm**
stock-dove, whose— e—cho re— sounds through the—

C7 braes,— flow gen-tly, I'll— **F** sing— thee a— **C** **Bb**
glen, — Ye wild whist-ling— black-birds in—

F song in— thy— praise; **C7** **F** My— Ma-ry's—a— **F7** sleep by thy **Bb**
yon thorn—y — den; Thou— green-crest-ed— lap-wing, thy

F mur-mur-ing— stream, — **C7** Flow gen-tly, sweet— **F**
scream-ing for— bear, — I charge you dis —

1 **2**
C **Bb** **F** **C7** **F** **C7** **F**
Af-ton, dis— turb not— her— dream. 2.Thou fair.
turb—not my— slum-ber-ing—

Medley 16

ROAMIN' IN THE GLOAMIN'

Words and Music
by HARRY LAUDER

♩ = 108

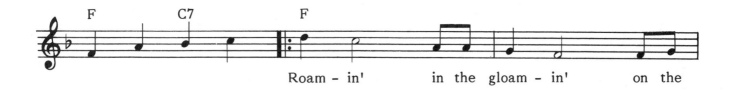

Roam - in'   in the gloam - in'   on the

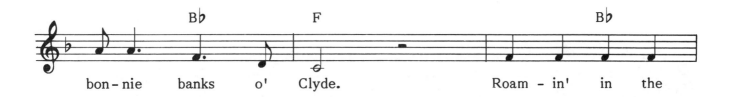

bon - nie banks o' Clyde.   Roam - in' in the

gloam - in' wae my las - sie by my side.   When the

sun has gone to rest,   That's the time that we love

best.   O, it's love - ly roam - in' in the

gloam - in'.   - in'. Aye, when you're

SAILING UP THE CLYDE

Words and Music
by WILL FYFFE

sail-ing up the Clyde, Sail-ing up the Clyde Back to bon-nie

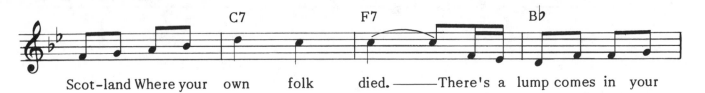

Scot-land Where your own folk died. ——There's a lump comes in your

throat And a tear you can-not hide When you're roll-ing back to

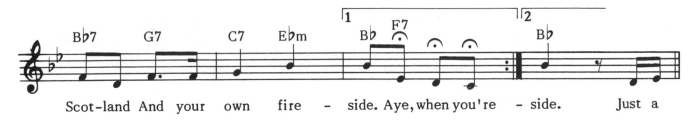

Scot-land And your own fire - side. Aye, when you're - side. Just a

JUST A WEE DEOCH-AN-DORIS

Words and Music by HARRY LAUDER,
WHIT CUNLIFFE & GERALD GRAFTON

wee deoch - an - dor - is, Just a wee yin, that's a'. Just a

wee deoch - an - dor - is, Be-fore we gang a - wa. There's a wee wif - ie

wait - ing, In a wee but - an - ben;—— If you can say, "It's a braw bricht

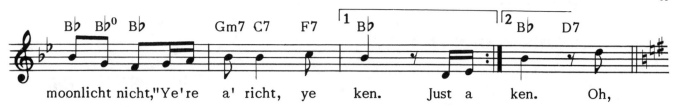

moonlicht nicht,"Ye're a' richt, ye ken. Just a ken. Oh,

THE KEEL ROW

TRADITIONAL

who is like my John - nie, Sae leish, sae blythe, sae bon——nie? He's

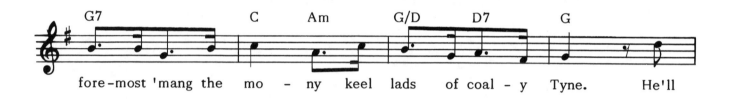

fore-most 'mang the mo — ny keel lads of coal - y Tyne. He'll

set or row sae tight - ly, Or in the dance sae spright——ly, He'll

cut and shuf - fle sight - ly, 'Tis true, were he not mine.

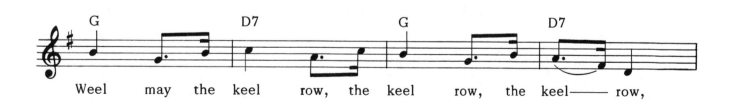

Weel may the keel row, the keel row, the keel——row,

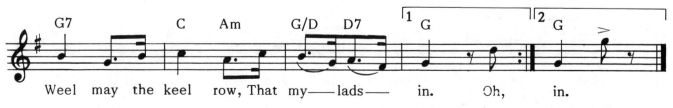

Weel may the keel row, That my——lads—— in. Oh, in.

Medley 17

COMIN' THRO' THE RYE

TRADITIONAL

Gin a bo-dy,

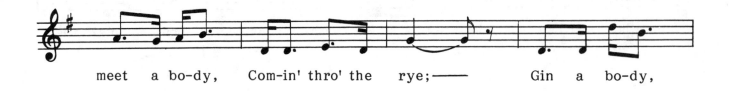

meet a bo-dy, Com-in' thro' the rye;—— Gin a bo-dy,

kiss a bo-dy, Need a bo-dy cry?—— Il - ka las-sie

has her lad-die, Nane, they say ha'e— I;——Yet all the lads they

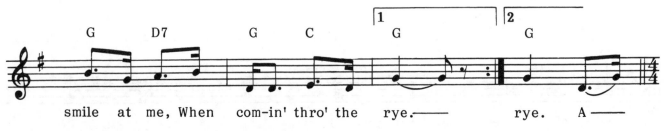

smile at me, When com-in' thro' the rye.—— rye. A——

THE ROAD TO THE ISLES

Words by KENNETH MACLEOD
Music Arr: MARJORY KENNEDY-FRASER

far croon — ing is pull-ing me a-way As —

take I wi' my cro-mak to the road, The —

far cool — ins are put -ting love on me As

step I wi' the sun - light for my load. Sure, by

Tum-mel and Loch Ran-noch and Loch - a - ber I will go, By —

heath-er tracks wi' hea-ven in their wiles; If it's

think-ing in your in-ner heart brag-gart's in my step, You've

nev-er smelt the tan - gle o' the Isles. Oh, the

far Cool — ins are put-ting love on me, As

step I wi' my cro-mak to the Isles.

ANNIE LAURIE

TRADITIONAL

1. Max - well-ton braes are bon - nie, where ear - ly falls the —
brow is like the snow-drift, her neck is like the —

dew, ——— And 'twas there that An - nie Lau - rie gave
swan; ——— Her — face it is the fair - est that

me her prom-ise true; Gave me her prom-ise true which
e'er the sun shone on; That e'er the sun shone on, and

ne'er for-got will be, } And for bon - nie An - nie —
dark blue is here e'e, }

Lau-rie I'd — lay — me down and dee. 2. Her dee. Should

AULD LANG SYNE

TRADITIONAL

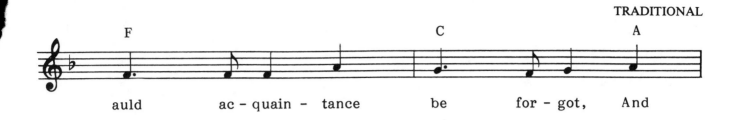

auld ac - quain - tance be for - got, And

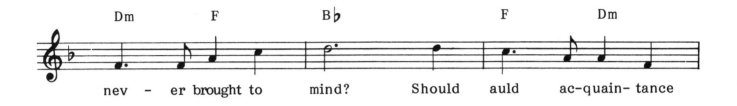

nev - er brought to mind? Should auld ac-quain- tance

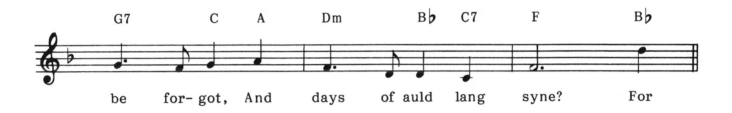

be for- got, And days of auld lang syne? For

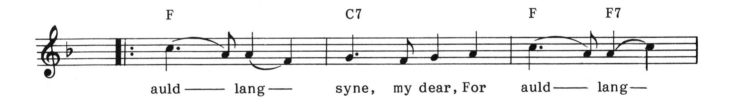

auld —— lang —— syne, my dear, For auld —— lang —

syne; We'll take a cup of kind - ness yet, For

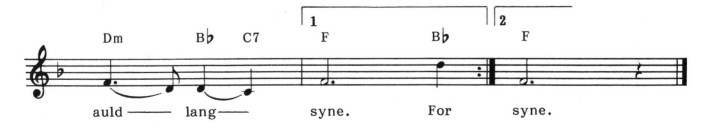

auld —— lang— syne. For syne.

Printed in Great Britain by Hobbs the Printers of Southampton 5/92